PEOPLE *of* IMPORTANCE

By the same Authors

IMPORTANT PEOPLE
SERIOUS BUSINESS

People of Importance

by the authors of
"IMPORTANT PEOPLE"

J. H. DOWD
Brenda E. SPENDER

LONDON: COUNTRY LIFE LTD. NEW YORK: CHARLES SCRIBNER'S SONS.

First published October 1934
Second Impression November 1934
Third Impression November 1935
Popular Edition October 1936
Reprinted November 1938
Reprinted October 1941
Reprinted November 1942
Reprinted June 1947
Reprinted December 1948

PRINTED IN GREAT BRITAIN BY
LOWE AND BRYDONE PRINTERS LIMITED, LONDON, N.W.10

Contents

CONTENTS

PEOPLE *of* IMPORTANCE

IMPORTANCE is a thing so entirely in the eyes of the beholder that it can grow to giant size or vanish to nothingness according to the point of view : and the same persons—Dante's " certain people of importance," for instance—can be both important and utterly unimportant—save to themselves—according to the angle from which they are seen. But the importance of the people whom Mr. Dowd has drawn in this book—real, living people, each and all of them—is, I believe, of a kind that no one can question, no eye fail to discover.

Mr. Dowd, stalking his admired quarry—"little game " that is still the biggest game of all—from park to perambulator, from school to garden, from country lane to city pavement, has put together here the unharmed trophies of his sport ; a collection of " heads " which includes the smallest and the largest of their kind, and some are obviously poor and some as obviously not, and some look very nicely dressed and some look even nicer in nothing at all, but all are plainly People of Importance. In fact, it must be acknowledged that, probably, no people of such importance for their age and size have existed for many years past—there are, thank goodness, a great many fathers and mothers about still, but, for various reasons, so very few children in comparison. The artist, dubiously surveying some of the one-child families in which he has found his models, asks me what their children in turn " are going to do for uncles and aunts ? "

But there is another sadder thing than an uncle and aunt shortage, bad as everyone, of course, would admit that to be ; these children who represent a whole family in themselves are in some danger from the very fact that all the admiration and petting and even all the anxious love that a father and mother might have spread over six children, or even eight or nine in luckier days, has all to be poured out upon one little head. The result is a Person of Importance whose life is spoiled by too much attention, too many treats, too many toys— the latest distracting his attention from the one before till none is particularly beloved—and by the conviction that there is no other person quite as important as himself anywhere about, a conviction which is never in the long run an additional source of happiness.

It takes years and generally some tears to teach a Person of Importance so deflected from the perpendicular, that the world is not really a system of which he is the centre, and there are cases where it is never realised at all, but the best schoolmasters to teach him are brothers and sisters, and the child who has none is unfortunate in that—even if his father and mother are wise enough to take their parental love in hand and give him only his due portion of its expression.

Apart from their rarity, however, these People of Importance can make no claim to being more important than their forerunners, and there is no likelihood that they will do so, for to every child its own importance is absolute : it looks out through its own eyes on its own world and the new untried, uncompared " me " is all it has to guess by or to serve.

Not only that ; the child, because so few disappointments have blunted its belief in itself and its own life, has an imagination which confers on it an almost boundless additional importance at will ; an imagination hardly limited even by the lack of knowledge or experience, for it is wonderful what original but satisfying use the smallest child, building an imaginary world, can make of facts or fancies which one would hardly have guessed had ever come within its ken. They can be great generals or queens—or milkmen— with all the proper accessories, and some very odd ones, merely at a wish ; they can own castles where no one grown up sees anything but a newspaper with holes in it hung up across a corner of the nursery, or drive flocks and herds before them on the strength of a couple of battered toy animals. How clearly I remember still the " Brownies," little toy horses standing perhaps three inches high, covered in something that looked like brown, pony skin and with tails and manes of black, real hair. Dearer than any doll was always the Brownie of the day, his neat, black hoofs, his round, brown hind-quarters were so real to me that I often thought him truly alive. Dark was the day when the last Brownie disappeared and was thought to have found a watery grave in the attic tank. And as long as I had a Brownie I was an intrepid rider ; races, reviews, the hunting field, all saw me at my best, for imagination made nothing of the fact that the horsewoman could have carried her steed on her little finger.

The small girl whose imaginary dog Charlie[1] used to go out shopping with her and her mother, and get into the way of the people on the footpath and run across the road in front of cars and be well scolded for such naughty tricks, probably finds it difficult to believe, now she is a grown-up young lady, that no such little, white terrier ever really existed as far as other people's senses served them. The child who saw fairy baskets of fruit on the slats of the Venetian blind in an old nursery,[2] and a fairy himself on the top of a pear tree in a London garden, may, for all I know, still, in middle-age, cherish a half belief in those lovely things which made her part of so strange a world to which no brother or sister had a key. The boy who for weeks at a time became, not Lord Nelson, for that would have been a kind of blasphemy, but the faithful Hardy of the kiss—not " Kismet," whatever the irreverent like to say—was really hurt when a grown-up person carelessly denied his identity. One and all they are instances of how, when we are young, we take,

> " Imagination, given us to bring down
> The choirs of singing angels,"

and use it to persuade ourselves that we are indeed People of Importance. And these people can use the power of imagination to glorify not themselves

[1] " Dog Stories from Punch " (Ingleby).   [2] " Important People " (*Country Life*).

ix

only but all that belongs to them, Daddy and Mummy, Nurse, the garden, and, perhaps more than anything else, toys and pets. Very few children think of a pet animal as anything but another person : a person who has somehow got under a striped, furry skin or wears rough-haired, white all-over garments and a tail, but a real person for all that. They look with confident eyes on the pet's possibilities, and even carry their animal friends with them in their loftiest flights. The little girl of seven who wrote a hymn, of which this is the most striking verse, was entirely sincere, as I have the best reasons for knowing :

> "O Lord, we ought to think of cats,
> Of lions, tigers and of rats,
> For they are dumb and sometimes blind.
> O Lord, shall we leave them behind ? "

There is, of course, a great deal of nonsense talked—and written—about childhood : after all, it is only a state in a continuous process. To go back to an old and wonderful simile, childhood is only the moment when the bird flying into the lighted hall has still some dew of the night from which he came upon his feathers : it is the same bird that flutters through the torch-light and the smoke who wings out again into the open air. He flies out into the same quiet night from which he came and we cannot know how sweet its silence and its fragrance and the cool skies above may seem to his timid heart.

It looks as though children themselves acted unconsciously upon this knowledge, seeing where their real importance lies better than we do. These people who are already so great in their own eyes, so adorable in those of their elders, continually base their claims to importance not on what they are but on what they will be. They are the hope of the world and of their homes, they are the mirrors in which older and sadder people see a bright reflection of their own earliest selves, they are the clean pages upon which the future may copy fair our past, but the importance to which they lay claim is not that of childhood at all. Their whole being is set towards growing up. The child is to become a big man, a soldier, a lady, a mummy ; that is what matters. And they are right, for childhood is only a promise, and the fulfilment of that promise, if it is to be fulfilled, must be in later life. When these important people in their play become heroes and heroines, knights and ladies, daddies and mummies, they do but rehearse parts that they must act as well as they may later on if the years are to justify our faith in them as People of Importance.

B. E. S.

EARLY

OUTLOOK

1

CHUBBIES

2

3

TOILET TIME

4

Monkey-Tail

FROM those beginning days, incredibly surrounded with love and warmth and sweetness and tender voices, when individual consciousness is first aware of itself, most children have a memory of some feature of nursery life, some recurring incident—bathtime or bedtime or even bread and milk for supper—that is clearer than anything else : with some it is the first time such and such a thing was seen, or seen and realised, such as the first rainy day when, looking from the nursery window, one saw the raindrops striking up again from the puddles and someone said, " Oh, baby, see the little rabbits." Yet it may be not seeing but feeling the texture of soft fur against one's cheek or the strange exciting taste of raspberries fresh from their canes and warm with the sun. The eldest boy's first memories were of being in his young mother's arms beside the drawing-room fire ; he does not remember her face or her frock, only the warmth and sweetness of her, the utter safety and comfort of hiding his face in her neck, of clinging to her darling hand. He has not remembered the lamp-lit room or the silver things on the tea-tray or nurse coming in to fetch him for bath and bed, nor what they played together, he and she, on the hearthrug by the fire. All he remembers is her love. But she did invent all sorts of games for her small son, and he would watch her gravely for a while and then his little face would lighten into sudden, lovely laughter and he would join in, tremulous with importance and delight.

Yet the most loving cannot read the mind of the most beloved always, and one day she made him a paper tail out of the last sheet of *The Times* that nobody—really—ever reads, and tied it on with tape and called him her " little monkey." But instead of laughing he stared at her wide-eyed, and then seized the paper tail and tried to drag it away. She picked him up hastily, untying the tapes.

Monkey-Tail—(Cont.)

" Aren't you Mother's little monkey, then ? "

He clung to her half-afraid that it might be true, that he might have somehow been changed so far ; so far taken away from her. He shook his head.

" Mummie's boy," he said through his tears.

Bath Night

DAVID had a very strong sense of order, though whether he had been born with it or whether his father and mother had grown it in him is rather hard to decide. I am inclined to think that it was his very own because he showed it when he was so little and, when he was quite a baby, liked everyone to do everything for him and with him in the same way every time ; any change of plan or hesitation as to how anything should be arranged quite horrified him. When he was nearly four his father and mother took him to stay right out in the country in a little cottage on a common where blackberry bushes and gorse grew and a few cows and ponies walked about. It was such an old cottage and so far away from any town that there was no gas or electric light and no bathroom and even no taps. All the bath water had to be drawn up out of a well and heated on the kitchen fire and then carried upstairs and, when it had been used, carried down again, so, to save giving the old lady of the cottage too much trouble, David's mother let him have only a wash in a basin every day and a proper bath on Saturday nights.

Such a change of plan naturally interested David a great deal, but the reasons were explained to him and he accepted the alteration, only taking a particular interest in " barf-night " and asking when it was coming every day of the week.

On the third Saturday of their visit, when the water for his bath was just being carried up to the little, low bedroom with its dark beams and uneven floor, David, all his toys put away, was standing at the garden gate waiting to be called in, and presently there were footsteps on the dusty road and

Bath Night—(Cont.)

a tramp came limping into sight. He was rather a dusty tramp, footsore and ragged and old, but he gave a grin at the sight of the grave little boy at the gate watching him so seriously. David's mother, leaning out of the window above, saw her son standing there in his blue smock among the heavy-headed white pinks and the monthly roses and southernwood in the little garden, and she saw the tramp outside the gate looking at him too. She had meant to call David in but hesitated, feeling that she might hurt the man's feelings if she did it before he had passed, so she was able to overhear them exchanging remarks.

"Good night, young gentleman," said the tramp.

"Oh hurry, man," said David, "det home quick. Don't you know its barf-night?"

PEDESTRIANS

Aren't legs wonderful !

8

Feet, too!

9

10

THAT first morning, when the family woke up and remembered that they had really and truly got to the seaside last night, there was, as Nurse said, no holding them.   Breakfast, for which everyone wore bare legs and sand shoes, was a pretence, even mummie's sternness could not get more than porridge and one piece of toast eaten by anyone, and then hats were crammed on and buckets and spades snatched up and across the parade and down to the shingle they went, and on and on across the wet sands till the tiniest green waves with little white frills on them were at their very feet.

"Hooray !" said the biggest brother.

"The sea, the sea !" chanted the biggest sister.

Fat Henry said nothing at all, but removed his shoes and simply splashed into the sea, making big bright spurts of white water leap into the sunlight from under his rosy feet.   Paddling, with shouts and cries and laughter, was in full swing.

Presently Nurse came down to the edge of the little waves with Baby, who was only three, and so, since last year, had forgotten that she had ever been to the seaside at all.   Baby was her family's pet and darling, so it was no wonder that her brothers and sisters, spattering through the clear water, came out to greet her.

"Baby, come and paddle," said one.

"I'll take care of you, darling," said another.

"Nursie, take off your socks ?"   Her nurse relinquished her little hand and stooped to carry out her suggestion.   But Baby, with a look of utter reproach, shook her curly head and drew back her shoes one after the other from Nurse's ready hands.

"Baby *not* walk-a-feets," she said.

Bread and Milk

TILLY had been ill, so Tilly was sent down to the seaside with Nurse and they stayed at the little cottage with the long garden, at the end of the bay, and every morning they walked on the sands and every afternoon Tilly had a rest on the little, white, grown-up bed, just like Nurse's, and every evening they went on to the beach again and found it quite different because the sea was doing something else, and at every meal time they had the same trouble as they had had at home : Tilly wouldn't eat. Of course the truth was that she had been ill and didn't want to, but the naughty thing was that she wouldn't even try. Poor Nurse was at her wit's end, for how is a person who has grown thin and pale with measles and hot weather to be taken back to London all brown and bonny after a fortnight at the sea if she won't eat properly ?

At first Nurse tried being very kind and getting Mrs. Skelton, who owned the cottage and looked after them, to cook Tilly all the things she liked best, but that was no good. Tilly merely shook her head and said :

" Don't want any," and when Nurse was a little firm with her even added, " Nasty stuff."

So, when that was no good, Nurse tried being cross with her, and at last, when she ate no breakfast at all, left her to sit alone at the table until she had emptied her cup of bread and milk. At first Tilly didn't mind a bit : it was very hot and she felt lazy and, sitting with both her elbows on the table, for they had made an ordinary chair high enough for her with big books and cushions, she could look out of the window and see the waves busy coming in and the children digging and paddling, and it was quite amusing enough. But presently the woman who sold balloons went by with lovely ones, red and blue and green and yellow, all clustered together, bobbing on the end of their strings.

" Nurse, I want a b'loon ! " she called.

Nurse, sewing in the bedroom which led out of the sitting-room, called back :

6

Bread and Milk—(Cont.)

" Well, hurry up and finish your bread and milk and we'll go and get one."

" Don't want any bread and milk," said Tilly, looking at the cold white contents of her cup.

" Well, you won't go out till the cup's empty," said Nurse, " and if you're not quick I expect all the balloons will be gone."

Tilly hit the table with her spoon and began to cry.

" I don't want nasty old bread and milk."

" Very well," said Nurse. " You're being a naughty little girl. I don't want to see naughty little girls." And she shut the door.

About ten minutes later the handle rattled and Tilly peeped into the bedroom.

" Cup's quite empty," she said with her most engaging smile.

" There's a darling, dear, good little girl ! Now we'll go and buy a nice balloon." Nurse went down on her knees to kiss her and, as she did, something odd about the sitting-room carpet met her eye. It had a dim, straggly pattern of pink flowers, and somehow they all looked different—and well they might ! In the middle of each flower was a small white blob of bread and milk. But the cup was empty.

The Good Egg

WHEN Tilly had been at the seaside for five days all the lovely, hot weather suddenly went away in the night, and the wind began to blow and the rain came "shooshing," as Tilly called it, in sheets and there was nothing for it but to stay indoors and feel cold. As Tilly had been ill and had a pale face and thin legs and no appetite at all, whatever was given her, Nurse felt worried. What use is the seaside to sick children if the sun won't shine ? If a child who has a sunny beach to play on fails to get better and take her food, what happens to one who can only go for a walk along the parade in between showers ? It was twelve o'clock, and Nurse and Tilly were both tired to death of their sitting-room and their bedroom and the few books and toys and sewing things they had brought down, before the weather cleared enough for them to venture out, wrapped up to their noses in mackintoshes and scarves.

But Tilly, once outside, began to jump along, holding Nurse's hand as she had not done yet since the measle germs first made her peevish ; she couldn't help herself—there was such a lovely freshness in the wet air and the smell of seaweed and newly washed sand blew in so strongly and made her feel so light and happy.

"We'd better turn back," said Nurse at the end of the parade, and Tilly would have been sorry but for a funny new feeling inside that made her quite glad to be going home. When they stood on the doorstep waiting for Mrs. Skelton to open the door she looked up at Nurse from under her blue sou'wester and wrinkled her nose, sniffing like a little dog.

"I can smell my good egg cooking," said Tilly. "Oh, I am hungry !"

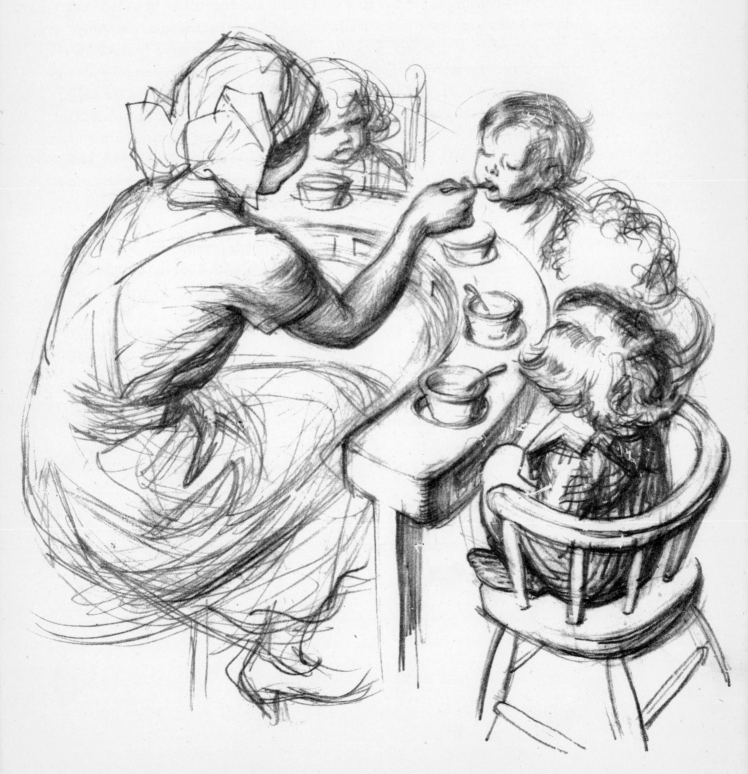

12

Her first day

15

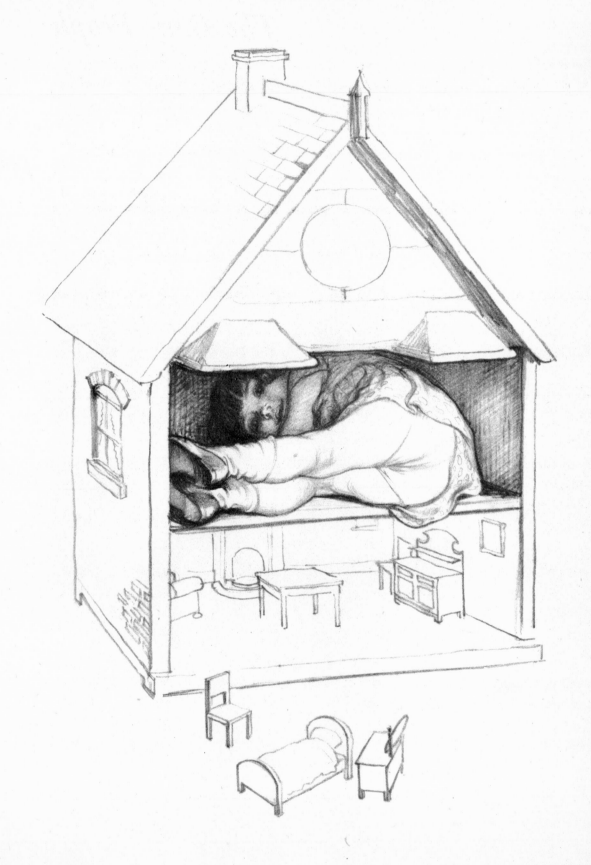

At home

16

The Bath People

THE two youngest reaped considerable benefits from the fact that they were twins : one was the pleasant practice, begun by their first nurse, of letting them share their bath, and out of that came the creation of the Bath People and their endless history.

There were four principal characters in the bath story, the leading lady being known enthusiastically as "lovely little Soaphiepart." It was no wonder that she was chosen for the heroine, she was so smooth and dainty and sweet-smelling and her shape was so elegant. She was a little helpless, perhaps, but so attractive that, of the three leading men, only Old Spongeeboy, who was a bluff, hearty person, a little Henry the Eighthish but much nicer, could fairly be said not to long for her society. It was in the true tradition of the stage that, though Old Spongeeboy and Flannelart and Scru-bart were always the same, the rôle of Soaphiepart was often given to a new actress ; or perhaps it was only that she wore a new dress, pale pink instead of yellow, and scented with rose instead of verbena.

Flannelart—for Nurse was of the school that never talked of " face-cloths "—was strong but very gentle ; he adored the lovely Soaphiepart and had no such joy in life as to wrap his long, loving arms around her and carry her here and there about Bathland as she ordered him : in cold weather he even took her once to Mount Hottap and turned it on to warm her, but Soaphiepart became so pale and thin under the treatment that he never did it again.

The saddest drawback about Flannelart was that, brave and gentle and loving as he was, he was a very poor swimmer, and when you think what a Venetian life the Bath People led and remember that his beloved the moment she was put into water sank like a stone, it is plain that his rival Scru-bart with his wooden back and bristles, hard and wicked and rough as he was, had him at a considerable disadvantage, for Scru-bart could swim like a cork.

The Bath People—(Cont.)

On the whole, the twins had modelled the Bath People's lives on scraps of opera and romantic plays which they had been told, and the incidents were sudden and dramatic, turning on the rivalry of the two young men for Soaphiepart's hand, with Old Spongeeboy as a sort of benevolent intervener and Lady Loofalight, who lived in a white enamelled basket high up the bathroom wall and belonged to the twins' daddy, as a combined angel, good fairy and Greek chorus.

The influence of opera might be traced to the fact that nearly all the characters sang their remarks or were accompanied on their journeys or in their struggles by a musical comment from the twins. For instance, Soaphiepart and Flannelart would be sailing some fine evening down Bath River in Soaphiepart's pretty, little, blue ivorine ship, The Dishieboat, to this song which, as it went to the tune of " Gaily the Troubador," had to have something the same words :

> " Gaily young Flannelart sailed on the sea
> With his pretty Soaphiepart
> After their tea."

" *You said it was almost their bedtimes," complained the elder twin to the singing one.*
" *Well, it is, only you do have tea before you go to bed, don't you? " explained the younger.*

> " Swimming came Scru-u-bart upset the ship,
> Flannelart, Soaphiepart, gave them a dip."

Then up came the wicked Scru-bart, swam against the Dishieboat and upset it, and Soaphiepart sank at once, a pink, glimmering shape in the milky water, and Flannelart went down more slowly after—diving, of course, and full of intent to save—but Scru-bart swam to him and held him back. Then Lady Loofalight, looking out of the window of her

10

high, white-enamelled tower, saw the horrid tragedy and called to Old
Spongeeboy, who was taking his ease in Tapland, to save

> Ding dong dell,
> Soaphiepart has fell (*This line came in a hasty parenthesis as there wasn't*
> Into the bath.   *room in the tune for the words*)
> Who'll pull her out?
> Spongeeboy so stout.

And just then, as likely as not, Nurse, coming in with the
warmed bath towels, would change all the bright, romantic
shapes into everyday affairs with one brisk sentence:
"Twins, how often have I told you that
it's right down naughty to leave the
soap in the bath?"

*   *   *

The Clergy Assistant

THE Padre at the English church was always considered to be "excellent with children." He did not expect them to know how to behave in church, but he told them at children's services in such a nice business-like way when to stand and when to sit, and where to find things in their prayer books, that nobody felt lost and muddled and, what was more important, nobody felt singled out for criticism or ignominy. In fact, everyone felt so happy and so much at home that it was scarcely to be wondered at that one day small William, tired of kneeling and quite convinced that he could tell the other children what to do just as well as the Padre did, rose suddenly from his knees and in a firm voice gave the order :

" All stand now."

17

18

HAIR!

19

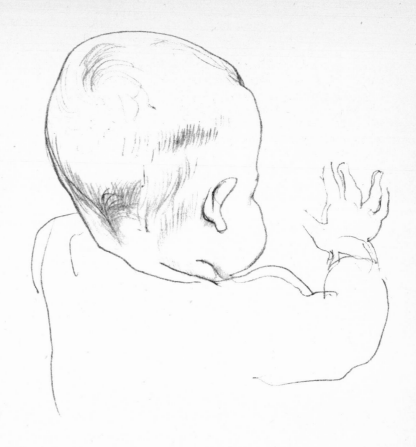

20

21

Shouldering his pride

The Naughty One

THE naughty one was generally at the centre of every storm; if voices were raised in anger or slaps were being exchanged, she was sure to be active ; if the forbidden tree was climbed, her red fisherman's cap was certain to be seen among the boughs ; if people got out of bed at night and played games in their sleeping suits on the stairs or pounced out on jellies going down to the kitchen from the dining-room, she was sure to be a ring-leader. She was quicker, more eager and fiery than her brother, not timid like her sister, or sweet and loving like Beebis : if someone annoyed her she liked to pay them out, and she hated begging anyone's pardon. So she really was the naughty one of the family, but a loyal, brave, stout-hearted little naughty one whom no one could help liking.

It was when she was only nine, a thin, dark child always busy doing something, good or bad, that her talents as a fighter proved their usefulness. The family was at the seaside, and, as so often happens, being at the seaside were less looked after and shepherded by nurses and governesses than was their wont, and the naughty one and the good one and Beebis and Beebis's beloved black rag doll Auntie Loo were all coming back from the beach together without any older person. It was not very far, but there was a little quiet bit of Parade to walk along, and two or three big boys were standing there talking and there were no grown-up people in sight.

Attracted by Auntie Loo's broad black face and grinning mouth, whether to steal her or only to tease, one of the boys snatched her away from her mistress's arms as she went by.

Beebis stood struck dumb with horror, too frightened even to cry. The other little sister wanted to run, but the naughty one took the matter in hand. With one leap she was on the enemy, she had snatched off her red cap in the heat of her anger and, holding it over her fist, she hit out left and right. She was small, but so fierce that the boys

13

The Naughty One—(Cont.)

were astonished into standing still and gaping. She made a grab for
Auntie Loo, and the boy who had taken her had not the presence of
mind to retreat. Thump, thump went the naughty one's hard little hands,
and then the defeated enemy was left behind and the three
sisters with their rescued treasure were flying for
safety. For once the naughty one had
been fighting and yet everyone was pleased with her.

* * *

AFTER the housemoving was over and they had really settled into the new house, and Daddy had hung up all the pictures and put up all the curtains and shelves, you might have thought that there could be nothing more for him to do and for David to help him with ; but there you would have been mistaken.

"Now," said Daddy, "we'll tidy up the tool chest—that's the next piece of work."

So out they went to the shed, and David, very business-like in his overall with the pockets, sorted screws and nails, and Daddy cleaned all the chisels and screwdrivers, and was very cross because on the rainy day when the furniture in its big van had been "riding," as David said, "all along England," some water had got into the tool chest, and some of the tools were rusty.

David was very much interested. He asked anxiously :

"If they'd only been wet a little tiny minute and then wiped on a big towel, would they have gone wusty ?"

He sighed with relief when Daddy answered him that in that case all would have been well. He was thinking of his bath at the moment and the danger that lurked in dampness, but when half-an-hour later he stumbled on the gravel path and bruised his knee he saw another alarming possibility in tears. He rushed to Daddy, stifling his sobs :

"Please, Daddy, wipe mine eyes. Please, quick, Daddy—they might wust !"

The Draught

WHEN Denis and David were quite small one of their favourite games was to make a house of chairs and play at living in it. All the chairs in the nursery would be piled together in the best way that their united efforts could contrive, and various toys were taken with them to their fastness when they went into residence.

It happened once in the winter, when their grandmother who hated the cold weather had been staying with them, that Denis was mounted on one of the further chairs, a small one perched on a big one, and his elder brother came pushing his way up between the others, spoiling their arrangement.

" Oh look," said Denis with a sigh, " he's a draught coming up between the boards ! "

PENNY sat in the second row of garden chairs—well, for Penny the angle of the chairs made it a rather lying-down sort of sitting unless she wriggled very hard and sat up with her bare legs sticking out in front of her and her strap shoes nearly as high as her shoulders, which did not look very comfortable. But Penny was not much concerned about that because she had never been to a play before and naturally accepted garden chairs as quite the proper thing in the stalls. Indeed, she sat as upright as she could, and never thought about chairs or of being uncomfortable, or even that plays were only plays, or of anything real, after a beefeater in lovely red had walked into the middle of the grassy stage and blown a bugle, for then the play began and the wind howled and the thunder roared—or if they did not the actors made you feel that they did—and the mast of the little ship on the stormy sea in behind the trees could be seen tossing to and fro most helplessly while the men on her bewailed their fate.

"Daddy isn't on the ship, is he, Auntie Jeff!" said Penny, and Jeff, who knew quite well what Penny was thinking, assured her that he was not.

"He'll be coming on soon—you wait!" said Jeff, and after that Penny hardly noticed the Prince and the sailors because she was so busy wondering when she would see her father. Would he come from the sea, like the sailors from the ship-wreck, or out of the trees where a little path ran away and was hidden by bushes? She was quite surprised when he really did come out of the cave on the right of the stage, that seemed to be really a queer sort of house, with a lovely lady, like a fairy-tale princess, with long, dark hair, hanging on his arm. Penny's daddy had funny clothes on and a funny hat that somehow made him look terribly grand, and the lovely lady called him "my dearest father," and altogether, to a person who did not know anything about plays but a great deal about that particular daddy, it was rather confusing.

Regent's Park—(Cont.)

But love allows no such trifle as confusion to deflect its stream ; Penny with an effort wriggled herself a little higher on her seat and waved her hand, waved again, waved so violently that the people in the chairs all round began to stare.

" Wait a little, darling," said Jeff.

Then Penny's father began to speak, and all the other people listened even more interestedly than before, since this actor was one of the great men of their own time speaking the words of a far greater than himself, and speaking them with majesty because this player was a poet too. Jeff, suddenly aware of something different in the poise of the round, fair head, looked down at the occupant of the next deck chair.

" Don't you like it, Penny ? "

Grave, lovely eyes, with tears just ready to fall, looked up at her under puzzled brows.

" Daddy won't smile at me ! " said Penny.

The Empty House

THERE is something about empty houses, even quite ordinary ones, that makes them much more interesting than a lived-in house, however exciting the people may be who have moved into it. Even quite ordinary little houses, little red ones in the middle of rows with painted front doors and a bow window on one side and another above, have a share in the fascination if only they are empty long enough ; and houses that are strange or lonely or stand in large, dark gardens become, as time passes, of such incarnate mystery that even to wait at the gate of such a one and pretend to yourself that you are going in can make your heart shake with a kind of delightful fear.

The children used always to look for empty houses on their walks, and peep over fences and through shrubberies and venture inside drives, if nurse were willing, and stand to wonder about them. Some they knew for months and felt were their own property, houses that were to be empty now as long as one brick stood on another ; some they only saw once or twice ; and some they lost because tiresome people, who could not appreciate the fact that these were empty houses by every law of nature, came and lived in them and hung white curtains at the windows and had the brass polished on the front door.

Once or twice they were lucky enough to go over an empty house ; there was a queer, long, low, dark cottage that they were taken into by a cousin, with whom they were spending the day somewhere in London. There were other people going over it, too, and one strange boy, who made faces, said that Cromwell used to live there, and that a stain of blood marked the floor in one of the rooms and could never be washed out ; all rather frightening then and rather bewildering when they were older and thought back to it. Then there was the tall old house in a terrace ; their mother had wondered whether they could not all be packed into it comfortably, and went over it with a young agent jingling keys and the children clattering behind. It had more stairs than any

The Empty House—(*Cont.*)

other house in the world, and such high ceilings to the rooms that one felt that no real family of ordinary people could ever have lived there and eaten meals and written letters and done home-lessons. It was quite, quite empty, but up in one of the attics, right under the roof, there was a baby's cradle, the only piece of furniture in the whole house, standing in a corner, broken and with a spider's web spun across it, and somehow it made them all feel miserable, and they were glad to come away.

Strangely enough, the best empty house was one which they saw for months every day of their lives, for it was next door to their own when they went to live in a county town in Wales. The two houses stood side by side, but detached from their neighbours, in a leafy, hilly street, and they were exactly alike at first glance save that one was lived in now and one was empty. When you looked closer you found other differences : the empty house was lower down the hill than their home, so that the wall dividing the gardens was low on their side and high on the other ; and there was a greenhouse built on to the back of it, broken and tumble-down but full of a growing vine ; and the garden, which had not been dug for years and years, was thick with bushes.

Very soon they were moved to go exploring. The big brother stood on the wall and lowered his sisters down into the strange garden and its stinging nettles ; then he jumped down to them, and they crept on, holding hands, and, stealing round to the back of the house, peered through its dim windows with little shudders of comfortable creepiness, and into its strange empty rooms, which were all the stranger because they were like a queer, inverted copy of their own home. But the strangest thing about the empty house was the loveliest ! When they came round to the further side they stood and stared, for a little stream— perhaps a trickle from a broken pipe underground—ran down at their feet, and all its course was marked with clumps of lovely, gleaming, golden monkey-musk in full bloom. That was why they called it " the house with the stream in the garden."

They went back often, never quite unafraid, ate the green grapes from the vine in the autumn and the little hard pears on the old, nearly dead, pear tree. But before Christmas time their parents moved again ; the house next door was still empty, the stream still ran in its garden, and next spring the yellow flowers would mark its course—for all they know it may be empty still !

* * *

The New Hats

THE twins, when they were little, always had new clothes at the same time and always to match, so, of course, there were two of the new hats with buttercups on them to go with the cream lace dresses. The twins were wildly delighted ; they each tried the other's on and looked at themselves in the glass, and though the hats were as much alike as the twins were, which is to say that no one could tell them apart, each declared that hers was much nicer than her sister's.

" Lovely, lovely hats," said Val.

" Dovey, dovey hats," said Vi.

" Chocotaw hats," said Val, who had vague memories of her elder brother's talk of Red Indians and their tribes and thought a " Chocotaw " was a sweet.

" Rockadore hats," said Vi ; and because, somehow, the word sounded like their funny poke-bonnet shape, " rockadore hats " the twins insisted on calling them.

A funny pair they looked that day when their Mother took them walking in the park, alike in height, in colouring, in little fat legs and round, rosy faces, alike in the famous hats sprinkled with buttercups. They had never had artificial flowers in their hats before and their pride was immoderate. When people turned to look at them, they held hands and laughed to each other.

" They're looking at our rockadore hats," they said.

IN THE PARK

23

25

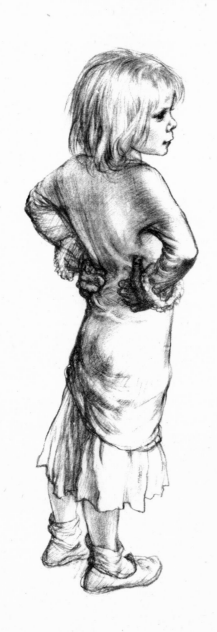

An important person
of experience

Horse power

Trying jam
on the dummy

LITTLE DADDIES

29

Affection

But it's not
his own cart!

It's an Ill Wind!

IT was one of those days when everybody seems to be naughty at once, and all the things that can't very well be deliberately naughty are sure to be tiresome.

In the Park Theophilus was trying to see just how bad he could be without making his Nannie take him home and put him to bed. A mile away, on the third floor of Patrick's Buildings, Micky Shea was cross because he couldn't very well be out in the street with the other boys, since his bad leg stopped him from walking downstairs and his father hadn't got back home at his usual time to carry him down—he went out so early in the morning that he had to come back to begin his night when other people were having tea. Micky, for his part, was trying to see just how long he could go on hammering nails into the window ledge before his mother, who was washing clothes at the sink in the corner, came across and fulfilled her threat of smacking him.

It was one of those days when there is a tiresome, teasing wind and yet everything is hot and unrefreshed.

Theophilus, playing at bouncing his beautiful purple air-balloon that Nannie had let him buy from the man at the crossing, said that a stone had got into his shoe ; Nannie, stooping down to see to it, felt cross because the wind whipped the short ends of her hair out from under her hat and it tickled her face. Micky, a mile away on the third floor of Patrick's Buildings, hit his fingers with the old hammer and began to whimper. Mrs. Shea, with the exasperation of those who are overworked and overtired, saw that her kettle had boiled dry and her washing was to be hindered.

It was really a perfectly horrid day : everybody felt it.

"Take care, Master Theo," said Nannie ; "don't leave go of the string of that balloon or it will be off in a moment."

Theophilus, who was really quite a dear little boy but spoilt, made a face at her and let go at once. Of course, he meant to grab the string again immediately, but the balloon had only been waiting for the chance and the wind was ready to help it. He grabbed, but he caught nothing. Nurse came to his help, but the balloon was above her head and the white string evaded her. Up it went, up, up, glistening and dancing, never prettier than as it rose a gay bubble of purple above the trees and the flower beds ; and Nannie and Theophilus stood watching it sail away.

It sailed and sailed and soared. Presently it came down a little, an eddy of air caught it and drove it this way and that, then it dipped, came a little lower down still, floated between the tall houses in a narrow street, found an open window under which a small, cross boy was sitting busy with something on the ledge. It bounced against the edge of the window and bounced away again. At that moment Mrs. Shea opened the door, the draught caught it, and the balloon floated in, hesitated, just brushed Micky's cheek, and landed on his knee.

"Mums," he called, bright and happy in his excitement, "look what I got !—What's come through the winder."

A mile away in the park, little Theophilus, drying his tears on Nannie's big handkerchief, looked up with wet blue eyes and began to smile.

In the Train

THE little boy was travelling by train for the first time in his life, and his view of it was one that would have amused any grown-up person who had long grown used to taking trains as every-day affairs. Of course, something—some faint tang of the smell of dust and tobacco smoke and leather that rose from the cushions so strongly when your nose was as close to them as it has to be at three years old, or one of the train noises—might have reminded a grown-up person of what their earliest train journey had seemed, but on the whole the first memories of most people are so covered up with later memories that they are apt to forget them altogether.

To the little boy everything was strange and exciting : the smell of the cushions and paint, the bare wood of the floor and the bristly feeling of the seat against his bare legs, the luggage rack like a little bit of the net from the tennis court, the straps that hung at each of the doors, and the painted numbers and letters that appeared here and there were marvels. And the song the train sang, " From Lincolnshire to Lancashire to get a pockethan'kersher "—but he had never been told the words—would have been the most wonderful of all, if it hadn't been for the old gentleman in the corner.

At first the little boy didn't believe that he was a real old gentleman : he thought that perhaps he was a stuffed old gentleman without a glass case, kindly put there as a species of ornament ; but when he rustled his newspaper that theory had to be abandoned.

When he blew his nose in a big, white silk handkerchief and stared at the little boy, it became quite plain that he was real enough, even his long beard and his eyelashes that stuck out so far over his eyes. When he grunted and felt his pockets, and took out a packet of sandwiches and began to eat them, the little boy watched him in such fascination that the scenery flying by behind the windows, the cows and horses and ponds and cottages and churches with high steeples, had no attraction for him at all.

25

In the Train—(Cont.)

"Don't stare so, darling," said his aunt in a low voice ; and she was quite glad when they reached their station and she could take him away.

But that night as she was tucking him up in the new strange little bed, in the new strange room where he was going to sleep, he gave her unconsciously the explan- ation of his behaviour.

"Where does the old gentleman that belongs to the train go bed ? " he asked.

*   *   *

Swing high!

Georgian

AT THE PAGEANT

34

THE head mistress, though her hair is white, has a girl's figure and a girl's eyes and, either for those reasons or some other less obvious, her pupils have quite definitely decided that, though she should be treated respectfully, there is no need to act as if her interests were any different from their own. They talk to her politely, but as equals and with none of that instinctive hiding of real desires and beliefs which is apt to blur the lenses through which the older and the younger look at each other.

A little while ago the head mistress decided to start a school aquarium. The oblong glass tank was small, but all that an aquarium should be ; soon there were suitable water-weeds spreading out their filmy leaves in it, there were water snails and curly ram's-horn water snails, big and little, and two whiskered cat fish belying their reputation for interfering activity by lurking on the pebbles at the bottom.

Said Evelyn to the head mistress, looking round from a long stare into the green under-water world:

" Would you like some tadpoles, please ? "

Her great friend Mary outbid her.

" Miss White, wouldn't you rather have tiddlers or sticklebats ? "— as London children call sticklebacks.

The head mistress assented.

" Anything alive, that likes still water, will be welcomed," she said.

While the bell rang for afternoon school, Evelyn and Mary came to her in her sitting-room.

" We couldn't get any sticklebats at the fishmonger's, Miss White," Evelyn explained ; " so we got half a pound of these—they cost six-pence ! "

" The man gave us one great big one at first, but we'd never have got it into the aquarium," said Mary.

And with the pride of those who have achieved, they set down among her books a large, damp newspaper parcel which, as it was released, wriggled itself open to reveal no fewer than four, large, alive and squirming eels.

27

Cheat

THE reason why one wants such and such a thing so terribly is often rather hard to remember afterwards ; that was what Helen felt about the flask of scent that she won fishing for bottles at the village fête. It was a pretty little flask, and " Jasmine " on the label suggested a lovely smell, but even that was not quite enough to account for why Helen set her heart on it so utterly. Perhaps it was that fishing for bottles is such an enticing sort of game, and so annoying because you feel that it is quite easy and you are bound to win and yet you continually find yourself losing.

At the village fête, so as to make money for mending the church and having the bells made to ring properly, everybody who wanted to play at fishing for bottles and win one of the flasks of scent or the bars of chocolate or any of the other prizes, had to pay a halfpenny for each try. Six children could fish at once, and when six had paid their half-pennies, Mrs. Cartright from the Green, who was looking after the game, said " go " and everybody tried to drop the big, wooden curtain ring that was tied to the end of their line over one of the tall, thin-necked bottles standing in a row in front of them. It sounds easy, and it looks easy, but the rings slipped this way and that instead of neatly fitting round their bottles, and there was so much shouting and laughing with six people playing that it made it more difficult still, and every time just as Helen thought she was going to manage to ring her bottle someone else did theirs and the game was over.

And Helen, every time she lost, got more determined that she would win and looked at the little " Jasmine " flasks of scent, where they stood on a table behind the row of bottles, with a more longing eye. She had twelve tries and had spent all her pennies but one, and was wondering whether Daddy would give her another sixpence, when big Timmy Jessop, who sometimes dug the garden or cut up firewood, came to play beside her.

28

" Haven't you caught nothing, Missy ? " he asked.

" Not yet," said Helen, " and I do so want to—I'd just love some of the jasmine scent."

" Well, I must get it for 'ee," said good-natured Tim, and then, just as the game had started again, the Vicar came hurrying up and announced that the cake-guessing prize had been won by kind Mrs. Cartright. Everybody's eyes left their fishing-rods for a minute to look round at this news and smile, everybody for the moment forgot the game to share in the pleasant excitement—everyone at least save Timmy. Helen felt a tiny jerk on her rod as though she had caught a little fish, looked, and found her fat, brown curtain ring safely set about the neck of its proper bottle.

" Timmy ! " she said.

Mrs. Cartright, beaming still, turned to her :

" Why, if you haven't won at last, Helen. You deserve a prize, you do. There's your scent bottle."

Everyone clapped and Helen took the little flask in her hot hand and turned away with a scarlet face that they all thought was caused by shyness at finding herself so singled out. She couldn't speak ; she could neither thank Mrs. Cartright nor tell her that she had not really won ; she could not even look at kind, stupid Timmy grinning at her, full of pleasure at the success of his interference.

Years afterwards, one summer holiday, she turned out an old treasure box and found a little green flask labelled " Jasmine " hidden in the corner.

" I wonder where that came from ? " said Helen, and then she saw that, though it had never been opened, all the scent in it had dried up long ago, and suddenly she remembered.

The Call of the Sea

WHEN Jimbo was twelve he went away to the training-ship. His father took him, and the last his mother saw of him was a grave face, rather too pale to make her quite happy about him, looking out of the railway carriage window, and an arm in an unfamiliar dark blue sleeve waving until the train began to go round the curve and the last carriages hid the first ones from anyone on the station. But when half-term came and brought an invitation printed on a gold-edged card with a crest on it, Jimbo's mother was the one who travelled down to the training-ship to see how things were going with him.

It was a grey autumn day, and Jimbo's mother was rather tired and a little inclined to be sad, perhaps because of that. The journey was slow and ugly, and when you got out of the train there was still a walk through a village, which was trying to pretend that it was a town, before, after making two or three wrong turnings, you came to the long pier that belonged to the ship. Jimbo's mother knew that it was the right pier for three reasons ; almost everybody who had come by her train was crowding down to it, a boat manned by cadets in the dark blue uniform was busy shipping them for the trip out to the *Lancaster*, and the ship herself—quite extraordinarily like you had imagined her—was riding at anchor in the near distance.

Jimbo's mother, having taken so many wrong turnings, was a late comer and so one of the people who had to wait for a second boat, and she was hardly sorry, because the lines of the old square-rigged man o' war, her tall masts, her white ports and her black hull, were so beautiful against the grey river and the wide sky with the clouds racing across it that looking at it filled up all your mind and left no room for impatience. Presently when, helped by a very polite cadet unbelievably young and unbelievably serious to a seat in the stern of the cutter, she began her journey to the ship, Jimbo's mother was still absorbed in its beauty. The ship grew taller, more majestic, as you approached, and when they passed almost under her stern-walk to make the gangway it was as though for a moment the years between rolled away, like the smoke above the sea, and the days when such ships followed Nelson's flag into the line of battle were no further from to-day than yesterday.

Jimbo's mother, as she climbed the long, easy wooden steps of the gangway, was still a little dazed and bewildered, and her first view of the deck, with that vague but persistent remembrance of the historic past strong in her mind, brought another confusion. She could not see her son, and yet there were so many small dark blue figures with gold-badged peaked caps sauntering two and two in arm or dashing here and there on errands ; and anyone of them might have been Jimbo, and no one was.

" Mother ! " said a voice and there he was, gravely saluting first and then shaking hands, and she drew a quick breath of gladness, looking into his darling face, and wanted to kiss him, and then remembered that his father had warned her against caresses, and refrained in time.

" Oh, Jimbo " ; she took his arm and hugged it against her side. " How lovely to see you. What a beautiful old ship she is—how I'd like to paint her picture."

" The Captain says everybody wants to do that, and his cabin's full of the things artists send him."

His mother looked at him and her smile wavered ; it was such a grown-up remark, so devoid of enthusiasm, it chilled her excitement a trifle, made her feel that her little boy had grown into a young man in the few weeks since she had seen him. She made a snatch at his childish interests in a sort of desperation.

" The rabbits are all awfully well, Jimbo, and Dinah's got a nice family of new babies."

" Oh, the rabbits," said Jimbo, and laughed. " I'd better show you round. We'll do the chart room first."

He dropped his arm from hers and led the way, and more and more

31

The Call of the Sea—(*Cont.*)

the illusion grew that this was not, except in looks, and even there he had grown taller and thinner, the little boy who had said "goodbye" at the station but someone very much older, more serious, efficient, competent and aloof.

The tour of the ship took time ; there were all sorts of things to see, the sick bay with clean white cots, the deck where at night each cadet slung his hammock, and the spot allotted to him was marked by the presence of his sea-chest with its white-painted lettering.

"New fellows get their hammocks let down on them at night a few times," said Jimbo in parenthesis with the removed interest of one who was no longer "new."

They found tea being served on the upper deck, and afterwards, down below, Jimbo shyly introduced his mother to the Captain when they met him, with a diffidence that would have been excruciating if that much-experienced man had not met his overtures half-way and as it were turned them inside out.

When dusk began to fall there was only a little while before the boat would put off that Jimbo's mother must take in order to catch her train.

"Half an hour more ! Oh, Jimbo," she said, " it's gone much too quickly ! What shall we do ? "

"Let's go below," said her son, and steered her down the difficult companion-way and along between the rows of sea-chests to the one that bore his name. They sat down on it side by side and for a little while they were silent. That sense of seeing back into the past was strong on Jimbo's mother, there in that long, low place between decks where the stark ribs of the ship showed so plainly, where the evening light through the deep square ports left so much darkness here and there. She seemed to see into a past that stretched back beyond the lifetime of the old ship herself, Trafalgar, the Armada, older battles still—the long chain of men who had gone down to the sea in ships to fight their country's battles—

and forward again, forward to this little son of hers and this strange demanding life that must carry him so very far away, that like some exigent vocation had already taken him from her into a world where mothers might not follow. Suddenly she felt the pressure of his head on her shoulder. He gave one glance round the darkening, empty deck and then his face was against her neck, his arm round her.

·" Mummie," he said in a whisper, " tell me about the rabbits and Dinah's puppies."

And she knew, with tears smarting in her eyes, that no career and no vocation and no hurrying years, not even fullest manhood, can take a mother from a child's heart any more than they can ever take a child from a mother's.

Kid Sister

THOUGH people have been so busy of late explaining things, nobody seems to have explained the curious natural law by which sisters are generally very proud of brothers, but brothers, at least big brothers, always seem to be rather ashamed of sisters. Jimbo's mother, who knew quite well that he loved his little sister, was almost annoyed by his coolness to her when, after weeks of looking forward and excitement, she took Kitty down to see him on his training-ship. Jimbo's mother was far too well-versed in the ways of sons to expect open delight or any demonstration of affection, but the brother, who had not seen his sister, owing to quarantine for measles, for nearly six months, received her with a coolness that was almost disapproving.

"Hello, kid," he said, "you've got more freckles than ever."

Kitty's round, pink face, beneath its powdering of golden freckles, went a shade pinker because she was just beginning to be a little self-conscious about them herself, but she was much too pleased to be with Jimbo, much too full of admiration for his grown-up look and his blue uniform and his peaked cap, for the way in which he had saluted like a real sailor before he shook hands, to be hurt for more than a moment. Besides, there was so much to see and hear, everything was so strange and so exciting and then, being a sister, she was not unaccustomed to the ways of brothers. In half a minute she was just as happy as before and ready to follow Jimbo round the ship, wide-eyed with astonishment and flushed with excitement. But in the *Lancaster's* chart room Jimbo pointed out that her fingers had left a cloud over some bright brass-work, and when she asked him questions about the rigging and how long the rope on the anchor was he said, "Rope! Good Lord!" and laughed. "Why don't you say 'string'?"

And he refused to explain things on the ground that she wouldn't understand if he did, and generally patronised and snubbed her till it was really quite a chastened-looking Kitty who came back from seeing the

34

sights. Their mother, divided between her wish to save Kitty from disappointment and her reluctance to show Jimbo that she was not pleased with him, was hardly in any better case.

After tea there was dancing below and, though Jimbo decided that he was not going to dance, his mother insisted on being taken to watch ; so down they went, down companion-way after companion-way, and on the huge deck deep in the ship found a merry crowd swinging to and fro under the big electric lights. It gave one a strange feeling to be sitting there far below the water-line, watching the blue uniforms and the pretty frocks dancing by, and to reflect what dark and terrible scenes, what searing toil, what fear, what blood and wounds, perhaps, this place must have known ; the walls were gaily draped with flags, and it was dedicated now on working days to nothing more sanguinary than boxing and gymnastics.

Jimbo and Kitty and their mother sat on one of the long forms arranged round the edge of the floor space and watched the crowd surging past, and Kitty looked eagerly at her brother and kicked her toe against the deck in time to the music of the piano and fiddle, but Jimbo preserved his air of one above such trivialities as dancing. It was quite a relief to their mother when he suddenly went pink, poked his sister hard in the ribs and said, in what was meant to be a whisper but in order to be heard above the noise had to be a little shout :

" That's the Captain."

" Oh, where ? " said Kitty.

" Dancing with a girl in green . . . well, a young lady."

Kitty looking this way and that discerned the right couple among the dancers.

" Oh, is that the Captain ? " she asked ; " I mean, I thought he'd have his medals on."

Kid Sister—(*Cont.*)

" Did you ? " said Jimbo with elderly sarcasm. " He only wears them in bed."

Kitty, not being sure whether he meant what he said and only quite certain that Jimbo was annoyed with her, subsided and sat in a little depressed heap until the dance was over, seeing very little but her own unhappiness and disappointment. It was Jimbo, getting to his feet in a hurry, red with excitement, and a new voice speaking that aroused her. The Captain was talking to her mother ; he turned to Jimbo :

" Well, if your mother doesn't want to dance, what about your sister ? "

" Kitty, sir ? " Jimbo's voice almost failed him. Here was the Captain, head of the ship, the finest man in the navy, the best athlete, the greatest hero, the cleverest, the keenest, altogether the most admired, in fact the greatest, man of our times—not to exaggerate—asking Kitty to dance with him.

" Will you give me this dance, Kitty ? " asked the Captain, shaking hands.

The little girl smiled and blushed and said something that meant " Yes, please," and they walked out into the gay crowd that was moving round again. Jimbo was left staring ; his world was standing on its head.

" Who's the pretty flapper the Boss is dancing with ? " asked a friend from his watch coming up beside him.

" That," said Jimbo, and his mother smiled at something in his voice, " that's my kid sister."

SCHOOL

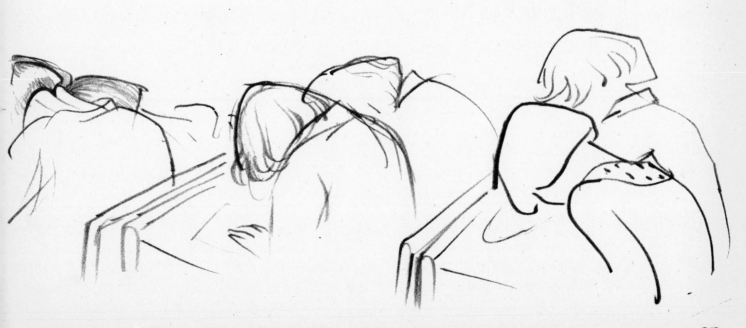

Milk-time at the
village school

36

37

Bag & baggage.

40

Eton v. Harrow

41

42

Not cricket

43

RURAL ENGLAND

44

The Hungry One

"IF Harold won't stop biting his nails," said their governess, " I shall have to get cook to send him up a piece
of bread. He must be hungry ! "

Harold's eldest sister looked up from the essay on
" Wordsworth and the Flowers " which she was copying
out in her beautifully neat hand and reflected that Miss
Pennington was really very clever, because nobody could
possibly go on doing a silly thing like biting their fingers in
the face of such threatened ignominy. But apparently
Harold's bad habit was too deeply ingrained for any fear to
stop it, and half an hour later cook made her appearance
with a crust of bread and a glass of water, and set them
down beside his Latin primer.

" Now, Harold," said Miss Pennington, " if you're
hungry eat that . . . you've no excuse to go on being so
disgusting."

The eldest sister, crimson from brow to delicate chin,
hardly dared to look across the table at the brother who had
endured such degradation. Had the plate and glass stood
at her elbow she felt that she could not even have glanced at
them, that her shame would have been unbearable. In her
sympathy she hardly knew whether to keep her head down
or to give him a friendly smile to show that she still loved
and admired him. That seemed, when all was said and
done, the kindest course ; she raised her eyes with an
effort and sat silent and aghast ; Harold, with the utmost
enjoyment, was calmly finishing the last fragment of his
crust.

The Prodigy

JOHN LANG was one of those little boys who early achieve a reputation for cleverness in their families and are listened to and watched by admiring relations, even in Scottish households, with an attention which may or may not be good for them. John's particular gift was a commonsense inventiveness and perseverance which made everyone predict that a "future" lay before him, and that all the great engineers and inventors and sometimes, it seemed, the philosophers would be obliged to look to their laurels before he was very much older. He himself, though he expected, as most children do, to be taken seriously, had no idea that he occupied so favourable a position ; his own outlook was his utterly unself-conscious concern, not how other people might be looking upon him.

It was while he was still a very little boy that a proud young aunt took him with friends for a day's sight-seeing, which included a visit to a big waterfall. Standing on the bank at the top they all watched the hurrying water slip over into the white cataract and dash down on the rocks below, and John, using Aunt Diana's outstretched hand as a rope, leant over the water a little further than anyone else was able to.

" Eh, it's bonny ! It's bonny ! " he said, coming back to the perpendicular. " D'ye ken what I'd do with it if it was mine ? "

Diana, with an eloquent glance in the nature of an aside, called the attention of the group to the prodigy's coming pronouncement.

" And what would you do, Johnnie, if it was yours ? " she asked.

John heaved a big sigh and, wiser than he knew, made answer :

" What would I do if it was mine ? Why, I'd just let it bide."

The Opportunist

NOBODY knows where Peter Pippet came from; as far as that goes, one can only suspect that it was raining cats, or rather kittens, that day when he made his appearance at the cottage, but, if so, it can't have been raining puppies as well; he was far too calm and unafraid for that, lying curled up on the warm earth of the flower-bed, between a root of white pinks and a tall blue anchusa. Clarissa, coming out with a cushion to sit on as her contribution to tea on the lawn, espied him, and Peter Pippet—that was not his name then, of course, or if it was no one knew it but himself—woke up, at least as far as one eye, the one on the top, was concerned, and looked at her.

"Here's a darling little kitty in the garden," said Clarissa, and proceeded to drop the cushion on the gravel path and pick him up, which one can only suppose was exactly what he meant her to do. Peter proceeded to make himself as charming as only a month-old "fitchy" kitten with a round white spot between his eyes and his nose, and a tail like a little speckled silk snake, can; he snuggled against her chin, he breathed in her ear, he patted her hair with little pink-padded paws whose claws were like the tiniest doll's pins, and Clarissa took him to her heart at once; but he need not have been so proud about it—she did that with all animals.

"May I keep him, Mummie? May I take him back to London?"

But Clarissa's mother had to say " No," and indeed Clarissa herself saw that it was impossible: was not their own Willy Ticket, tabby and beruffed and terribly self-important, waiting for them at home, and was it likely that he would endure the presence of a young, frisky and distinctly common stranger without either breaking his own heart or the stranger's head?

Clarissa and her mother were only to spend another fortnight at their cottage, so Peter Pippet's prospects were undoubtedly gloomy. He was living on the fat of the land now, petted and played with all day and

39

The Opportunist—(Cont.)

tucked up in a warm basket at night, but, alas, the hours of this luxury were running away fast and what was to become of him when the shutters were put up at the cottage windows and Clarissa and her mother went home?

"I'm going all round the village asking everyone till someone bedopts him," said Clarissa, and so next day her fat little legs carried her from door to door till hardly a house was left unvisited.

"Please do you want a very 'tractive kitten?' Clarissa asked, looking up earnestly into the face of whoever answered her knock; but the village seemed to be extremely well supplied with cats and no one wanted another: even the lady at Yew Tree Cottage, who made a pet of Clarissa and called her "Pollie" for short, said:

"No; I am afraid he will chase my chickens."

But Peter Pippet apparently knew more of the matter than one might have expected; when Clarissa went across to Yew Tree Cottage next time he followed her; he scrambled up to the kind lady's lap and breathed in her ear and patted her hair just as he had with Clarissa when he first introduced himself to her, and then he went and did all the same pretty tricks to the lady's husband. The result, of course, was that he stayed there and learnt not to chase chickens. But next year when Clarissa came down to the country again and rushed across to Yew Tree Cottage to see him, instead of doing any of his pretty tricks for her, when she tried to pick him up, he arched his naughty back and spat at her.

Eighteen Eighty Seven

FOR weeks there had been a growing knowledge in the nursery, something like dawn gradually lighting up the shapes of trees and hills, that Jubilee day was coming and, when it came, would bring delights and wonders such as no one had ever seen before, not Daddy or Mummie or Miss Practiss their governess or—which was much more remarkable—even cook herself. As the day grew nearer it began to be seen that these delights and wonders were to include a procession, with the Mayor and Councillors in their robes and the fire brigade in their helmets and all sorts of other people in all sorts of other interesting clothes, going to church to return thanks to God for having let Her Majesty rule so long and so well. The children with Miss Practiss were going to watch the procession from the windows of their father's office. Then there would be a dinner at the Mayor's parlour and a dance in the assembly rooms and illuminations in all the streets, but these were rather for grown-up people, except the illuminations ; yet anyone who was really good all day, and for a week before that, was to stay up late and be driven round in the pony cart by McIlroy to see them. But the thing that really interested the children most was that in the afternoon the Mayor was going to have a whole avenue of little trees planted in the pleasant wide street that ran uphill out of the town. He was going to ask some ladies to plant a tree each and name it, and the Mayor, laughing, had said to Daddy :

" Bring your eldest daughter there and let her plant one."

Dorinda wasn't exactly Daddy's eldest daughter then, for he had only two, but even Betsinda, who was good at arguing about things when she wanted to, couldn't argue on that account that she ought to have been the one to plant the little tree.

So, though they all went down to the tree-planting, it was Dorinda, in the little blue pelisse with a red border that Mummie had knitted for her, who was really most concerned. The others stood with Miss

Eighteen Eighty Seven—(Cont.)

Practiss in the crowd, and watched while the Mayoress flattened the earth round her little tree with a very bright spade and called it " Victoria," and the Vicar's wife named hers " Lord Shaftesbury," but Dorinda stood with Daddy among the important people and knew for the first time in her life what it must mean to be an eldest daughter. Daddy looked down at her.

" What are you going to call yours, Dodo ? " he asked ; but Dorinda only wriggled her little fat hand in his and shook her head.

And when all the ladies' trees were planted, Dorinda's turn came. Daddy held the spade so that it wasn't too heavy for her ; a gardener held the little tree in its hole, and it stood up brave and straight when they patted the bright brown crumbling earth down round it.

" Now you must christen it, missy," said the Mayor.

" Yes—what's to be your tree's name ? " said Daddy.

All the ladies and gentlemen and the crowd and Miss Practiss and the others listened for her reply. Dorinda looked at the little tree, and then at the crumbly yellow earth round its roots.

" Brown sugar," she said.

Country faces

46

47

48

THERE are some people who seem to be strangely out of their proper place in things ; artists born into families where no one cares for art ; keen, questioning minds that never meet those who can speak their true language ; old, sad people alone in households where everyone else is busy and gay ; children who might as well be the only ones in the world, they know so little of their own kind.   Little Alexander was such a one ; he was an only child, and he lived in the end house of the tall grey row near the park with his father, who generally wasn't there, and when he was there was always busy either in his study among his papers or in his garden among his choice rock plants, where Alexander had to be careful not to step on anything, and generally did and got himself sent indoors.   Besides his father there was Mrs. Mack, the housekeeper, oldest of the elderly household, and Annie the house-parlour maid, and the woman who came in to help and the gardener, every one of them almost, if not quite, old, so that a little motherless boy in a sailor suit seemed as odd and out of place there as a butterfly in a city street.

Little Alexander was delicate, so the doctor did not wish him to begin lessons, and Mrs. Mack was too fond of him to care for the idea of any merry, young girl as his nurse or governess taking her place in his affections.   His father had cut himself off from social ties in bitterness at the time of Alexander's birth, for it was just then that his young wife had died, so there were no friends whose children could have been his companions.   He went for a walk every day either with Mrs. Mack or Annie, and played on the lawn when it was fine, and when it wasn't, in his nursery at the top of the high house where the window looked out on a tangle of green boughs, save for a week in spring when it was a transformation scene of pink apple blossom.   And often he was very lonely.

As lonely children will, he invented wonderful games and kept himself " good " for hours over them, asking Mrs. Mack for the oddest properties with which to achieve his efforts.   That was why when, one spring day, just after the apple tree had shaken down the last of its pink petals, he asked her for " lots and lots of paper bags and a big sack " she was not particularly surprised.

" What are you going to do, Master Alexander ? " she asked.

" I'm going to make a b'loon," said he ; and that sounded so satisfactory that Annie was allowed to carry up to the nursery a clean old sack that had once held fibre for his father's bulbs and the big basket from the cupboard under the kitchen stairs, where all the paper bags that had come from the butcher, the baker and the candlestick-maker since the last spring-cleaning, had been put away.

All day long Alexander was busy blowing out paper bags and tying them up with short lengths of sewing cotton off a reel he had borrowed from Annie, and tucking each one, as it was ready, inside his sack. And all day long Mrs. Mack and Annie and the woman, very busy too downstairs because spring-cleaning time had come round again, were glad not to be bothered to do more for him than call him down for dinner.

Late in the afternoon the " b'loon " was ready, the sack was full and little Alexander had tied a piece of string round its mouth and made a loop to put his hand through. Then he pulled the nursery table up to the window-sill, and looked out into the heart of the apple tree and down, down to the green lawn ever so far below. He dragged the balloon up on the table, took its string in his hand and, never doubting that it would carry him flying gaily over the bright garden and across the park, bent his little, sleek, round head, crept through the open lattice and stood on the window-sill.

His father thought, then, that it was the disorder of spring-cleaning in the study which made him restless and sent him, for the first time in months, upstairs to see how little Alexander fared ; afterwards he wondered whether the impulse might not have had another lovelier, stranger source. He stood, what seemed to him a long time, petrified

with terror on the threshold of the nursery, staring at his son.   Perhaps
the boy felt his presence, for he looked round from the window.   His
father spoke, gulping, breathless, in terror :

" Alexander ! "

The boy stepped back.

" Oh, daddy, this is my b'loon," he said.

" I know . . .   I know."   His father's arms were round him,
and his father was looking what Alexander called
" funny " ; but after that day Alexander was
never quite so out of place in the household, nor his father ever
quite so far away.

* * *

45

The Baa

BEEBIS, much younger than her sisters and brother, was their pet and treasure; they were always at her service; if she made demands upon them it was taken as a compliment ; if she deigned to chuckle at something designed for her entertainment, the one whose efforts were so rewarded walked puffed up with pride. When they went to live at the seaside, while she was still too little to do more than toddle, her brother discovered an unfailing key to her favour.

On a small piece of waste land not far from their house, feeding on tussocky dry grass and penned in by strong railings, was a big white goat, and the brother soon found that the sight of a crust of bread would always bring him trotting to the railings, narrow nose twitching, slanting yellow eyes fixed on the dainty. He would sniff it for a second, then bare his teeth and take it, turning his horned head sideways to reach the level of the outstretched hand. As he ate he would watch his visitors, tossing his head now and then, standing with a kind of miniature magnificence on his small neat hoofs.

Beebis called him the " Baa," and " the Baa " became her particular joy. If she was merry she wanted to be taken to see him ; if she was naughty and had no wish to face the consequences, she would beg one of her slaves " Take Beebis to see the Baa."

If she was told to do anything she did not wish to do, that was her method of escape. The little soft arms were held out.

" The Baa ! Beebis see the Baa," she said.

A dozen times a day she and some attendant brother or sister stopped at the railings of the goat's field, and while the elder made him a suitable offering the younger stood and watched, round, pink-cheeked face solemnly intent, breaking from gravity into a delighted, deeply gratified chuckle as the Baa munched his delicacy.

A day came when the house at the seaside had to be given up ; when it was necessary to take the long journey north again, and that with

46

Feeding time

51

52

53

54

forebodings very different from the hopes with which the family had travelled south.   The children knew no cause for sorrow, but inevitably it was reflected in them ; the mother, brave as she was, could not make the journey happy or even pleasant.   By the time that they were all settled in a hot, crowded train, waiting for the second half of their journey to begin, no one was comfortable, but it was Beebis who expressed what everyone else was feeling.   From her mother's knee she held out coaxing arms to her brother, for he had never failed her yet, her small face smiling up under its blue fur-trimmed bonnet :

" Take me to see the Baa ! "

Our Bird

BETTY'S book is small and shabby and written very nearly two hundred years ago, as can be told because when she began it she dated it most punctiliously "May the 5, 1758." She seems to have kept it for about six years, a sort of combined diary and cash account, and there is no hint as to how old she was when she wrote, her spelling being possibly a matter of period rather than of age. But there is one entry which marks her as young in heart if not in years. " Our Bird died January the 29, 1760." There it is, jostling items which record the marriage of Thomas .Southernwood to " hannah weeler " and the deaths of " Dame Timbrill " and " Mrs. Markes at ye king of prusia "; " Our Bird," with his capital letters and the meticulously stated date of his demise, is as good as anyone of them all.

It happened much too long ago and too obscurely for it to be worth while to speculate what kind of bird he was—this small thing that won the love of a family and made hearts happier by his singing and sadder when he ceased—or why he died, but this entry in an old diary may stand as a sort of epitome of the child's attitude to pets. What happiness they give, what chasms of misery yawn when, under fur or feather, the small heart is no longer warm.

And how extraordinarily the birds and animals recognise in children something different from what they find in grown-up people : as it were, make excuses for their shortcomings as master or mistress and extravagantly admire their virtues. Sometimes it almost seems as though the dog who wags his tail under clumsy petting and the cat who purrs even though she is picked up against her will were saying to themselves, " There, there, only children, you see , they don't know any better ! It's not for us to bite or claw the little dears."

Sometimes, though, the animal has its quiet fun with the children—like the old brown curly dog on which it was everyone's ambition to ride who always just let you get on his back and then abruptly sat down spilling you on the ground, or the cat who delighted in lurking behind doors or gateposts and springing out to pat the thin, bare legs of his small mistress as she passed by.

The children on their side—perhaps enchanted to find themselves so closely in touch with another world, looking at life in however small a degree through other eyes—the children seldom or never adopt the " just an animal " attitude where a pet is concerned, be it bird or rabbit, cat, dog, white mouse, baby lamb or glittering grass snake.   It is a person, a friend, and when the day comes to write its epitaph, in words or tears, they write it with dignity and capital letters as Betty wrote in 1760 " Our Bird."

The Prayer

WHEN David was about six he went through a time of being very rude and rough: sometimes he snatched things and broke them, sometimes he shouted, and almost always if he asked for anything it was in such an ugly, rude way that his mother had to make him ask again and again till he spoke more politely. One night he had been put to bed early for such behaviour, and his father, when he came home from London, not liking to miss saying goodnight, went upstairs on tiptoe so as not to wake him up if he had fallen asleep.

As he reached the door of his little son's room he heard a voice speaking and stayed his steps.

" Please, God, make me a good likkle boy," said David. His father waited, but what he heard next was a surprise ; David spoke again, but this time very precisely in a very grown-up voice.

" Certainly not, David," he said, evidently answering himself, " certainly not, when you ask so rudely ! "

DAVID had lived all his life in Wales until he was four years old, and then his father and mother took him to see his grandmother in London. In spite of his sturdiness and determination he was such a very small person that a visit to the Zoo and to one of the big toy shops were the limit of his dissipations, but in every omnibus and tube-train, as he went on these excursions, his bright eyes were watching everything : he did not talk but he looked.

"What do you think of the tube, David ? " asked his father. David said :

" Nice."

"Lots of people, aren't there, David ? " said his mother. David smiled and snuggled his hand in hers. But, walking down Oxford Street, very small and upright in his white coat and leggings, with his curly head bare and a new toy engine clutched under his arm, he was suddenly moved to make a pronouncement.

" I like this village," said David.

Thistle-Down

WHEN Beebis was a tiny baby and there was no school and no governess, and the others often seemed to have nothing to do, their mother, who had all the loveliest ideas in the world, suggested that it would be possible, if they all worked hard, to make her a fairy pillow to sleep on in her cradle.

" Oh, what's a fairy pillow, Mummie ? " Betsinda asked.

" It must be the softest pillow in the world," said Dorinda. The brother listened and said nothing ; it scarcely does to take much interest in such matters, when both age and the fact that you are a man have made you so evidently a superior.

" What is the softest thing in the world ? " their mother asked : and then they knew that the fairies stuff their babies' pillows with thistle-down.

So all that month the children went here and there in the lanes and along the cliff-tops above the blue glitter of the sea, looking for thistle-down, and sometimes they caught the thistledown parachutes as they flew past them, but most often they put a warm, small hand on a thistle-head that was just about to start floating away, and caught so many thistle parachutes at one grasp that they laughed at the little tailor in the fairy story who called himself " Seven at a blow," and called themselves " Seventy at a grab." Their mother and Beebis, sleeping in her perambulator, went with them, with a flat linen bag, into which the thistledown was thrust as soon as it was captured, and by and by the bag was full, and their mother sewed up the open end and put a pink and white silk cover over it with a frill, and Beebis slept on it and everyone felt very proud.

What the effect of a fairy pillow was likely to be no one guessed then ; they peeped in at her in her cradle, and saw how pleasantly the thistledown made a nest for her little round, brown head—and that was all. It might, perhaps, had they been a bad fairy's thistles, have made her grow up as feather-brained as if the thistledown had got into her head ; but, luckily, all the fairies who had thistledown parachutes on the East Coast that year were good ones, and all the pillow did was to make her so much of a good fairy herself that everybody loved her.

But the odd thing was that when, one day when they were all nearly grown up, Dorinda and Betsinda and Beebis remembered the thistle-down pillow and went to look for it, though they hunted the house over from attics to kitchen, and even undid the covers on two small cushions in the drawing-room which might have been the thistledown pillow inside a new dress, they never found it, and no one ever remembered giving it away.

The Bogey Hole

AT first one of the most attractive things about the new house was what the boys and girls called " the bogey hole," though nobody else, not their father or mother, or either of the servants, thought much of it. A house in a row in a town is to most reasonable people a poor exchange for a house in a garden in the country, but to the children the mere fact that everything was different made it exciting, and there had been nothing like the bogey hole in the house in the country. That was one of its charms, another was the difficulty with which anyone larger than themselves must explore it. The entrance, through a rough doorway on the top landing, nailed up until they prised it open, was so small that though a grown-up person could just squeeze through if it were necessary to look at the dusty water pipes that ran along one wall, nobody could possibly enjoy doing it. For the children the doorway was large enough, and at first the excitement of tight-rope walking along the beams in the floor, thinking that one unguarded step on the plaster in between might plunge one straight through the bathroom ceiling with horrid noise and mess and bumps and horrider punishment to follow, was enough to make the bogey hole an excitement.

The part you first came on through the little doorway was nearly square, lit by a window high up in the wall, for this was the end house of the row ; on the other side there was another wall, but it did not run right across : beyond it there was a dark corner, which everybody supposed was nothing more than an alcove. It was when they played in the bogey hole on a long, wet day that, greatly daring, picking their steps from beam to beam, they felt their way into it and found that it was a long passage. The first time they went a little way and came back ; then, next, somebody announced a little glimmer of light, a sort of greyness at the far end ; presently they established the fact that their house and the other end house of the row had bogey holes joined by the

54

In the farm-yard

55

56

57

Tickles!

58

And who are you!

59

The fairy cottage,
Pullborough, Sussex.

60

BUSY BEES

61

62

SHY!

I

63

64

65

HAY DAYS

long unfloored strip running across the back rooms of the other houses right under the roofs.

I cannot tell you, or really expect anyone who was not among those children to understand, what the bogey hole came to mean to them, the magic, the adventure of those dark spaces all their own, the breath-taking thrill of knowing that you crept along the joists over the heads of strangers who never suspected your presence, who went on living their lives reading, eating and talking and working, and had no faintest inkling of the unknown who walked above them.

They brought their secret joy to an end by their own choice, when scoldings for dirty hands and torn frocks and trousers had had no effect, on the day when a strange, sad cry, rising up from below the floor, told them that someone in one of the houses below was crying. They were used enough to crying themselves and that could be understood, cut fingers, broken toys, home-sickness when you first went to school, any-one might cry for them, but this was different, this was grown-up crying and it made them afraid. The plaster floor must have been badly cracked over the room where that woman was weeping, they heard her so plainly they even caught a word of her sorrow, and something, some cold wind from the places where grief goes bare, chilled their happy hearts. They crept back very quickly to their own part of the bogey hole and out on to the landing.

" It isn't fair," said the eldest brother, shutting the little door, " to hear people when they don't know you are there. We shall have to stop going up the long passage."

" The bogey hole isn't really ours ! " said the second. " I vote we don't go in again."

And they never did.

The Old Gentleman

THE old gentleman was very, very old ; so old that he had been an old gentleman for a long time, and was different in his ways and the things he did and wore from the old gentlemen who had only grown into old gentlemen since he had. He lived all alone, except for people who nursed him and looked after him, and put food on his plate, and took his arm when he moved from one room to another, but generally he did not know that he was lonely. His mind had gone away from to-day and lived in different yesterdays, sometimes young yesterdays, and sometimes even childhood yesterdays, and a kind of mist hung, like a veil, between him and real things most of the time, though now and then it parted for a moment and he looked through unsurprised, at to-day. This generally happened when a stranger came to see him ; for he had been a very great man in his time, and there were still people who loved the books he had written and the wise and kindly spirit which they had shown to the world, and those people would come long distances sometimes only to sit with him for half-an-hour. And if he realised their presence and talked for a little while in a tired, small, old voice, but with all the wit and brave humanity they had loved, they would think themselves well repaid and, when he grew weary, go softly away from his curtained room full of tenderness towards him, and quiet in their hearts as though it was for the last time.

The old gentleman was very far away from to-day that summer evening when, because the sun was off them, the long windows were standing wide open and the little boy who was staying next door, when he had pushed through the thin place in the hedge and toddled up the garden path, could climb in over the threshold and stand, holding his toy engine in one hand and the red curtain with the other, and stare.

The old gentleman was so very quiet, sitting over by the big writing-table with his white beard on his breast, that, although he was strange, the little boy was not afraid but came closer, and then closer still, and

56

then stood and looked, very near, one pink hand with the toy engine in it actually on the white blotting paper where a few inverted impressions of the great man's signature made a dry, spidery pattern. For some reason beyond grown-up understanding, the little boy was attracted, sorry too ; he crossed one fat foot, with its white sock limply dropping down to the brown shoe, above the other.

" Would you like to play with my engine, poor man ? " he asked.

Slowly the old white head was raised, the tired blue eyes opened in the wrinkled face without surprise ; with no effort to explain his visitor's presence, the old gentleman accepted it.

" Play with your engine ? " He smiled, very tremulously he put out a withered hand and took the toy.

" A funny little engine ! " he said, looking down at the yellow wheels, the bright green of the boiler, the absurdly tall purple funnel ; and, as he looked, he stepped away into a yesterday that had gone by long before he had been famous, long before he was even middle-aged. He was in a sandy, sun-baked valley, and he saw big boulders on near hills cut against a shrill blue sky, and a train that had stopped with a jerk and a grinding of brakes ; there was a hiss of escaping steam and a stranger sound—the ping, ping of bullets which came from somewhere behind the rocks and passed his head. The stock of a gun kicked against his shoulder.

" Yes, of course I'll play, little son." He passed the engine back to its owner, who did not think it strange to be called " little son " any more than the words seemed strange to the man who used them and had not spoken them for the sixty years in which his son had been a memory. " You shall be the people on the train. . . . I'm the hillmen. . . . The valley. . . . Where shall we make the valley . . . wasn't there a toy gun . . . ? "

The little boy stared. They stared at each other. And suddenly

The Old Gentleman—(Cont.)

the little boy was afraid and turned and went, clutching his toy, looking
back now and then when he had something to hold by.   He scrambled
out through the big window and away down the garden path.

For a while the old man waited for him, then his head sank
lower.   The little boy and the toy engine grew dim,
faded from his thoughts : slowly, slowly the
spark of life that was in his brain
illuminated the memory of a
different yesterday.

*　*　*

Four-Leaved Clover

NEVER the time and the place and the loved one all together, or two loved ones uncomfortably jostling each other on the same spot; that was Dorinda's hard fate.

For months past she had spent hours creeping over the lawn on her hands and knees looking for four-leaved clover and, when they went for picnics, often refused to play with the others because the hunt was up and, being a child of extraordinary perseverance, entire lack of success had not yet discouraged her.

For a week, ever since her mother had taken her into Webber's big shop to buy them and the lovely young lady behind the counter had fitted them on, smoothing the wrinkles out of each finger one by one, she had looked forward to wearing her first pair of real kid gloves. They were white and very dainty and fastened with two buttons and had a little round " window," as her small sister called it, in each palm, and Dorinda, when Sunday came and Miss Practiss took them for their morning walk and she wore them for the first time, could hardly contain herself for the admiration that they aroused in her.

As usual the children's walk led them back to the church to meet their father and mother as they came out from morning service, but to-day the sermon had been long or the children were early and, while the lovely lifting sound of the last hymn came out to them through the open window, they waited on the little green outside the churchyard gate. And quite suddenly, when she wasn't really looking, Dorinda found her first four-leaved clover, down in the grass almost under her shoes.

" Oh, Miss Practiss," she almost shrieked in her excitement, " I've found a clover! I've found a lucky clover! "

" Oh dear," said Miss Practiss, " don't pick it! You'll stain your new gloves. You'd better leave it there."

" I can't. Please let me pick it. It's all my luck for years and years."

Four-Leaved Clover—(Cont.)

Kind-hearted Miss Practiss wavered.

" Well, take your gloves off and I'll carry them."

Take her gloves off, her beautiful new gloves, just when everyone coming out of church was going to see her, Dorinda, in real kid gloves ! Leave her clover, her lucky clover, when she had found it after so much looking ! Dorinda, standing there while the Vicar's voice, giving the blessing, floated out of the quiet church on the still summer air, seemed to herself to be torn into two pieces.

When the congregation came out they had the honour and pleasure of seeing Dorinda in her new gloves, but Dorinda has often wondered since, when things have been most provoking, how much she lost because she left the four-leaved clover on its root ungathered.

The Great Uncle

GREAT uncles are sometimes very old gentlemen, uncles' uncles or something of the kind, but that sort of great uncle is rare. Irene's great uncle is quite young, at least he seems quite young to grown-up people and quite old to Irene, so you can guess roughly what his age is, and he isn't a real uncle at all but one of the kind who come to stay and get called uncles, because they are uncles in everything but being born so. That is, they like swinging you on the lawn and they talk sensibly about interesting things and never call you " Baby " or tell you to run away and play.

Irene's new uncle is so remarkably nice that when people began to get ready to go to evening church that first week-end when he stayed with them, and Irene found that he was going, she asked if she might go too. In Irene's village evening church is often in the afternoon, because the Vicar has another church in another village and tries to divide himself up fairly between them. Irene's mother never makes her go to church in the afternoon, because on week days she generally rests then and her mother is afraid that, without her afternoon sleep, Irene might be tired and naughty in church. But when she asked to come it was another matter ; and nurse dressed her in her frock with the flowers on it and the Sunday hat with a white bow and her silk socks and gave her a penny out of her money-box to put into the collection, and Irene walked away down the drive and across the green and up the church-yard path very happily with her mother and father and her new uncle and two or three other people, and when they got into church managed to sit between Daddy and the new uncle just as she wanted to. Of course, she ought to have been good, having had all her own way like that, but the afternoon was hot and the hymns were ones she did not know, not " All things bright " or " There's a Friend," which she could have enjoyed singing ; and though it was nice to sit next to the new uncle it didn't actually make church more interesting to a very little girl.

61

The Great Uncle—(Cont.)

So during the sermon Irene looked round for something to play with, and what more obvious than the collection penny which was lying hot in the palm of her hand, tucked into her little, white, cotton glove by nurse to keep it safe?

She dragged the penny out, looking up at her Daddy and at her new uncle to see if either of them was looking at her, and she shook it between her two hands and she pretended to write with it in her hymn book and did all sorts of things, and presently, when they stood up to sing, she found a big crack at the back of the book rest and pushed it in. Of course, she never meant to lose it. She meant to put it a little way into the crack and take it out again, but the woodwork of the pew was old, the crack deeper than she knew; quite suddenly the penny was gone and, even as, hot with fright, Irene looked round at Daddy, there was the collection plate just being handed to him and coming to her next.

Here was a horrid punishment: she had played in church and lost her collection money, and the plate was coming and she had nothing to put in it! It was the sort of thing that was almost too bad to be believed in; the end of the world would have been far, far easier to bear, and goodness knows Irene worries enough about that. But the end of the world would be everybody's end of the world and the collection plate going by without her penny was all Irene's. As she stood in shame something touched her hand. It was a penny, not hers, but another penny, and it was in the hand of the new uncle and he was sliding it into hers. The plate came and the penny went into it! Irene was saved. The new uncle, who, as this occasion proves, was really a *great* uncle, looked down and grinned at her.

VILLAGE WEDDING

ARRIVAL OF
"JUBILANT
JOLIFICATIONS"

K

CIRCUS!

73

74

CHRISTMAS IN
THE TOY SHOP

View points

Conjuror's Hook

SOMEBODY said that Donny was rather too young to go to the village fête in the Vicarage gardens on Whit Monday, but his brother and sisters begged hard for him and he himself, having been filled full with their high anticipations, said most plaintively :

" Donny did want to see the cungelor."

So then everybody agreed that he was—generally—such a good little boy and so clever for his age and no trouble at all—usually—and nurse put his clean white shirt and knickers on him, and his big, round Sunday hat and his hated white shoes, and told him that he was not on any account to take them off to-day, and he was packed into the back of the car and driven away, most happily singing to himself :

" Donny see cungelor."

And he did see the conjuror, and made quite sure of that by holding tight to his sister's frock and saying, " Donny wants cungelor " every few minutes until the performance began.

When the Vicar rang a large bell and shouted out in his best big voice that he had grown when he was a sailor's vicar in a navy ship, " Professor Ruddigore is now about to begin his famous exhibition," all the people who heard told all the people who didn't and they came crowding down to the lawn and sat in a large circle on the grass, and some on chairs—the Member of Parliament and the Lord of the Manor, and old Mrs. Fellows who had rheumatism. And little trickles of people who had been in the garden, looking at the dark lilac or the pond, or playing tennis or throwing balls at the shy cocoanuts, came joining in until there was quite a thick ring of them all round the little table and the attaché case in the middle that belonged to the conjuror.

The conjuror had a grey suit on and brown boots, and was perfectly ordinary from them up to his necktie ; then came a big, low collar almost a frill and then a long, pale, serious face and the oddest hat, like a bathing helmet covered with bright buttons. It looked very funny, perhaps because the rest of him looked so just like anyone else, and also because he did not seem to feel at all funny himself.

Donny sat, in the front row of the people watching, on the grass with his legs crossed, a foot in a white shoe in each hand but not dreaming of undoing them ; his mind was far too well occupied, and he did not take his eyes from the conjuror from the first moment when he found a whole pack of playing-cards in the Vicar's hat to the last when he seemed to cut Ronnie the milk boy in two by tying a rope round him and getting two other boys to pull the ends, which would have been rather frightening, only Ronnie didn't seem to mind. Really he was a very wonderful conjuror ; he put a walking-stick right through the bottom of a glass and then mended it again ; he burnt Mr. Perry's pocket handkerchief right up and then put the ashes of it into a jam jar and poured some water in, and took the handkerchief out again clean and dry just as it started and, which was really the most wonderful thing of all, when he had something in his hand, say a big steel ring or a ball or a handkerchief that he did not want at the moment, he would say :

" Oh well, we'll just 'ang that on that 'ook up there till we want it again."

Then he would throw the thing—whatever it might be—up into the sky with all his might, and as far as anyone watching him could tell, it stayed there.

Donny, staring round-eyed, with the smell of trampled newly-cut grass coming up to his nose, the sun shining warm on his back, saw a lovely inside-the-head picture of the high blue sky all over useful bright hooks on which you might, if you were only as clever as the conjuror, hang anything that was a bother to you and never have to take it down again.

When the conjuror finished, Donny heaved a sigh and went off solemnly with his big sister to tea at one of the little tables in the garden, and afterwards to watch her fishing for bottles ; indeed, he was silent all the rest of the afternoon, silent even in the car going home when the others were talking like a flock of starlings and Mummie said :

" Poor Donny, he's tired !   But he has been good ! "

But nurse did not think him quite so good when both his new white shoes proved to be missing and no search in the car could discover them.

" What have you done with your shoes, Donny ? "

Donny smiled.

" Where are your shoes, Donny ? "

He looked at her with his head on one side and his blue eyes at their very brightest and most innocent.

" Gone on the cungelor's hook ! " he said.

And, since no one had noticed when he took them off or what he did with them and they were never seen again, the conjuror's hook was probably as good a place as any in which to look for them.

The Tap

RODERICK was one of those children who like doing things for themselves: he was always asking, "May Roddy do this?" "May Roddy do that mine own self?" Sometimes his independence was a blessing to his mother and nurse, sometimes quite the reverse: and sometimes, though very rarely, when he had begged to be allowed to do something unhelped the task defeated him. It was on such an occasion that, having teased and entreated to be allowed to turn the hot water off for himself, he was left in the bath alone with strict injunctions to stop the inflow as soon as the water reached his knees. His mother, in the nursery next door, was just wondering whether he had forgotten when a little naked figure appeared in the doorway.

"Mummy," he said, pink-faced with anger and hot water, "I can't turn the tap off—it's too fluent."

The Bright Penny

MUMMIE and the new baby sister, and Daddy and the new baby sister's own nurse, and the new baby sister's perambulator, and all sorts of baskets and hat-boxes and dressing-cases, had all got into the cab with the white horse and been driven away to the station, and Betsinda and Miss Practiss were still on the front-door step where they had stood to wave goodbye.

As long as you could wave they seemed to be still there ; *you* waving to *them*. But the cab turned slowly out into the road, it passed behind the fir tree by the gate, and they were gone. And when they were gone, when suddenly there was nothing—nothing—when Betsinda could still feel where her cheek had pressed against Mummie's for the last of her kisses, and how her fur had snuggled against her neck, and yet she was gone—oh, then Betsinda's heart was wrung with the empty pain of parting. She stood, tears streaming down her little rosy face under the straight dark fringe, tasting dimly, faintly, the agony that, sooner or later, tears the happy fabric of life and leaves it beyond any mending.

" You'd better come down to the toyshop and spend that lovely new penny Daddy gave you. Would you like that ? " said Miss Practiss, and presently Betsinda, only catching her breath a little with the memory of a sob, was trotting, her hand in her governess's, down the long hill into the town.

In the very first side-street was the little dark shop with a stick-out window where the children always bought their toys, and there, when Betsinda on tiptoe had peered through the small, square window panes at the treasures displayed behind them, they went in, down two surprising steps just inside the door with a bell on it, and looked round at a hundred more delights.

At first Betsinda wanted to buy something very grand with her new penny, but after all it was only a penny, even if it was a new one, and by-and-by the choice narrowed down to a small doll with a pig-tail that

67

The Bright Penny—(Cont.)

you could really plait, not just painted-on-china hair, and a lovely little green tin wagon drawn by two purple oxen, at least they were purple on the sides that were outside : on the sides that were towards each other, they were only flat and tin. But, in spite of that, there was something rich and foreign about them and their little cart, and Betsinda chose them. But half-way up the hill going home, she said :

" I wis' I'd bought the likkle, likkle doll, too ! "

" It wouldn't be ' too,' it would be ' instead,' " said Miss Practiss. " You couldn't have both."

So it is in life ; if you choose the ox-cart you lose the doll ; if you have a bright new penny to spend, it is only because you have been left behind lonely. Suddenly Betsinda threw her ox-cart from her and burst into tears.

" Mummie ! Mummie ! " she sobbed, " I want Mummie ! "

Now and Then

SOMETIMES when you live in the older people's world you are allowed, just for a second, to look back into the one in which you lived when you were young. Odd, unimportant things may be the winds which blow away the mist that hangs between now and then, letting you take an instant's glance through ; quite foolish, meaningless things they are sometimes. The smell of tar in the hot sun and for a fraction of a second memory is keen ; you do not think yourself young again, but you know in every fibre of mind and body what it was like on a summer afternoon, so many years ago, when they were loading coal on a tramp steamer by the north pier and you and the others stood to watch the crane swing over one more sack and one more and then yet another, and were late for tea.

Sometimes the suddenly sharpened memory is less definite ; a brown horse with shining quarters, polished hoofs and a trim mane goes past, and for a flash that wonderful clear-cut sharpness with which such things stood out focussed on the uncrowded mind and memory of a child is remembered—not recaptured, never recaptured now.

If your childhood went by near the sea there will probably be no wind that blows back the mists more surely than the off-shore breeze. Suddenly the complex world will show simple, clear-cut, limned in a few bright colours ; a heart that beats very steadily now will flutter for a second on the edge of that exultant leap to hope, to life, to far horizons that used to send you shouting to the water's edge, as though to touch the foam were the beginning of making its secret your own.

The horizon held the secret, and the deep preserved it from our eagerness then : the horizon holds it yet, but we do not believe that it will be told us here.

TA TA!